ISBN: 87191-093-4
Library of Congress Catalog Card Number: 75-174894

EAGLES of the Valley

JULIAN MAY

Illustrated by Rod Ruth

Creative Educational Society, Inc., Mankato, Minnesota 56001

Autumn frosts touched the trees in the Mississippi River valley, turning them to red, orange and yellow. Cold winds blew down from Canada, where winter had already begun. And riding those winds, soaring high above the river, came the bald eagles.

They came alone, or in small groups of parents with one or two full-grown young. They followed the river valley southward, seeking a wintering place with unfrozen water. For they were fishing birds, taking almost all of their food from rivers and lakes.

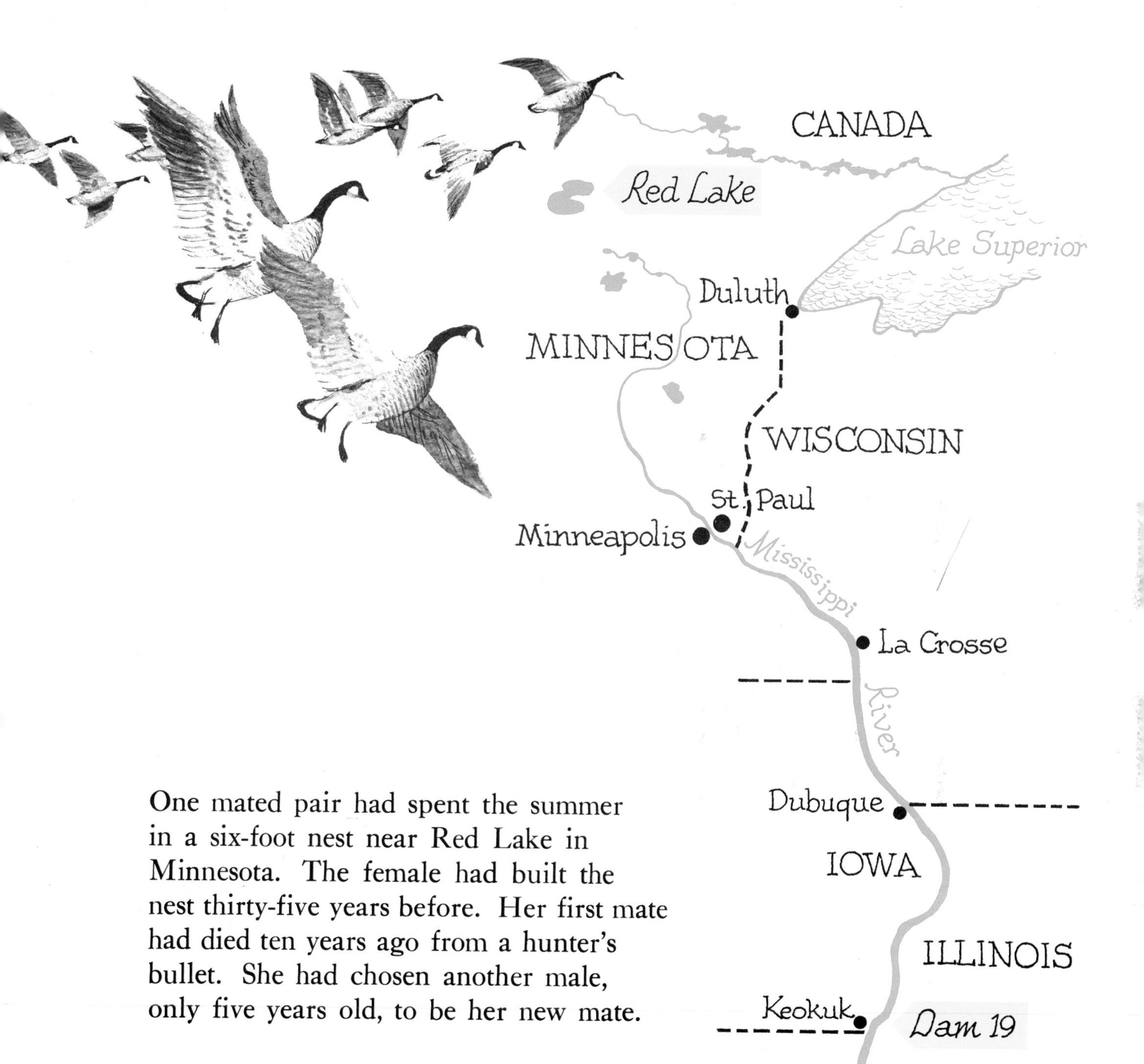

One mated pair had spent the summer in a six-foot nest near Red Lake in Minnesota. The female had built the nest thirty-five years before. Her first mate had died ten years ago from a hunter's bullet. She had chosen another male, only five years old, to be her new mate.

Almost every year she had laid eggs, and the two parents had raised young that usually flew south with them in the fall. But this year, the eggs had not hatched. The shells were very thin. When she tried to warm the eggs with her body, she crushed them. The chicks that were growing inside had died.

The male and female eagle had not understood why their eggs had broken. They had looked at them for a long time, then covered the shells with moss from the floor of the huge nest. All through the summer they stayed near, defending the nest from other eagles or from owls that would have settled there.

Now, with the coming of winter, they flew southward, down the valley to Illinois. They came to a place the river people had named Cedar Glen, the wintering place they had always used. Settling in a tall sycamore tree, they rested for the night. Nearly seventy other bald eagles roosted in the trees around them.

When dawn was about to break, the great birds rose into the gray-pink sky and flew toward the nearby Mississippi. Below them was Dam 19, one of many built across the river to protect the land from sudden floods, and to make boat and barge travel more easy.

The waters flowed swiftly over the dam spillway, as over a waterfall. Boats passed the barrier through locks at the side. The spillway tumbled the waters so much that they did not freeze, even during the coldest weather, for a distance of two to four miles below the dam. This was the place where the eagles hunted, together with ring-billed gulls and ducks.

They flew to riverside cottonwood trees, where each had a favorite branch that served as a fishing perch. The mated pairs often sat side by side, their white heads gleaming in the sun, the females slightly larger than the males. Immature eagles, colored dark brown all over, sometimes perched near their parents.

WARNING
DANGER
KEEP AWAY
FROM DAM

The birds scanned the water with eyes far sharper than those of a human being. The slightest flash of a fish body sent an eagle dropping toward the water, golden legs extended, to grasp its prey in hooked talons.

The successful fisher would return to the perch to feed. Sometimes a male would share his catch with his mate. But the adults did not feed any of the immature eagles.

The adult eagles wasted very little time getting a full meal. But the immature birds were less expert. They often missed the fish. And they wasted some of their time trying to seize the goldeneye ducks that bobbed in the turbulent waters. The ducks had only to dive to avoid their clumsy attackers.

By mid-morning, when the sun was high enough to heat the land and water, air currents began to rise upward. The eagles took advantage of them and went soaring, hardly beating their great wings at all as they circled up hundreds of feet into the air.

The female of the Red Lake pair did not circle as high as the others. An unusual weariness had laid hold of her this winter. She felt almost too tired to fish, and she had been grateful to her mate for bringing her some food. She did not soar for long, but went to perch on a large river island where the eagles often sunned themselves.

It was not long before most of the other eagles joined her there. The great birds sat almost motionless on the sycamore trees of the island. As the sun followed its daily path, the birds turned slowly so that its rays would warm their bodies. From late morning to late afternoon, they spent most of their time sunning and preening their feathers.

At about four o'clock it was time to feed again. And as the sun went down, they all flew to the night roost in Cedar Glen, where steep hillsides kept out the chilling winter winds.

A bird, like a mammal, has a body that is warmed from within. Each body cell consumes fuel, like a tiny furnace, and helps to warm the whole body. The fuel itself comes from the food the creature eats, or from its body fat, which is stored fuel. That winter, the temperatures in Cedar Glen dropped very low. The sick female eagle found it harder and harder to fly.

Her mate brought her food, but it was not enough for her needs. Her body began to change and use the fat for fuel; and as this happened she became sicker and sicker. For her body fat was full of poison. . . . It had come from the fish she had eaten over the past twenty years. The fish had taken in poison when they ate tiny plants and animals in the river. The tiny living things had taken the poison from the river itself.

And the poison had first come from the green fields, the beautiful orchards, and the handsome cities along the banks of the Mississippi—and along the banks of the hundreds and hundreds of smaller rivers and streams that poured their waters into it. Men had sprayed the land with insect-killing chemicals—with DDT, dieldrin, chlordane, and others—and the poisons had passed from the soil and into the waters.

The female eagle's body had been storing up these poisons for years. One kind had caused her body to make eggs with fragile shells. Another kind affected her liver, an important body organ. Poisons had gathered in her fat cells. And when the fat was used as body fuel, the poisons passed into her blood. On a very cold day in February, the female eagle fell lifeless from her perch. Her mate flew down to her, but he could do nothing. Drifting snow covered her body.

The male eagle, younger than she, had not taken in so much poison. Neither had the other eagles in the glen. Although some became weak during the long winter, no more died. When April brought a sudden, very warm spring to the Mississippi Valley, the birds began to fly north again, toward their nesting places.

The widowed male eagle flew alone to Red Lake. But with his mate gone, he lacked the will to defend the nest. Another pair of eagles drove him away and took it for themselves.

For several days he perched among some snags near the lake's edge. He paid no attention to the dark immature eagles that roosted nearby, young birds that would not grow their adult feathers until they were four or five years old. But then one day a strange eagle, larger than he, appeared.

The bird stared at him with deep-set, golden eyes, then took to the air while uttering loud cries. It was a young female, newly matured, seeking her first mate. He dropped from his snag and let the winds carry him up to her. For more than an hour the two birds wheeled and soared through the air together. Then they went to build a new nest.

The female did most of the building, while he helped bring branches, rushes, and other materials. When she finally had the nest the way she wanted it, she laid two white eggs about the size of hen's eggs. Both eagles were very proud of them, and both helped to warm them while life grew inside.

The young female eagle had also eaten poisoned fish, just as the other birds had. But the chemicals had not yet gathered to a dangerous level in her body. After thirty-five days, one of the eggs cracked. But it was not a cracking that brought death to the chick inside. Instead, it brought life. The eaglet was ready to hatch.

The little bird tumbled wet from the shell. He seemed all feet and beak. As he lay, making faint cheeping sounds, the other egg began to crack. The mother helped the second eaglet to emerge; then both parents looked at their offspring for a long time. Finally the mother settled her body over her young. The father bird went flying away. It was time for him to find food for his new family.

ABOUT BALD EAGLES

The bald eagle, emblem of the United States, is about 30 to 33 inches high and has a wingspan up to 7½ feet. The body and wings are dark brown, with a white head and tail in the adult birds. Immature bald eagles are brown mottled with white, attaining adult plumage when they are about four years old. Young bald eagles are easily mistaken for golden eagles or for large hawks.

Bald eagles are thought to mate for life. From two to four eggs are laid each season. If all hatch, the young may struggle against each other in the nest, with the weakest perishing. Both parents help feed the young. They may also help the immature eagles for some time after they leave the nest. Bald eagles in middle North America feed mostly on fish. They also take dead creatures, and will kill birds and sometimes mammals that are slow-moving, sick, or weakened. Only rarely will they take domestic birds, such as chickens.

Once common in most parts of North America, the bald eagle is now rare except in Alaska and parts of Canada. Scientists estimate that there are only about 500 active nests left in the "lower 48" states. Many of these are in Florida and in the upper Mississippi Valley. Hunters have killed bald eagles for sport and in a mistaken belief that the birds killed poultry. Today, laws protect bald eagles from hunters in all states, but the birds are still shot by mistake or by poachers.

After studies proved the harmful effects of certain pesticides on wildlife, laws were passed banning their use. However, leftover chemicals are expected to remain in our lands and waters for at least the next 20 years. During all this time, they will affect the health and the eggs of eagles. The birds normally live for a long time—perhaps more than 50 years. Have we acted in time to prevent them from becoming extinct? Only time will tell.